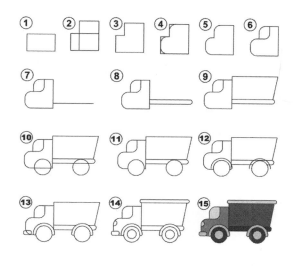

How to
Draw
Cars, Trucks, Planes, and Things That Go!

DP Kids

Learn to Draw Step by Step!

Learning to draw doesn't have to be hard. This book will show you how to draw all types of vehicles one step at a time including cars, trucks, trains, motorcyles, boats, planes, and many more. All you need is a pencil to get started!

Each diagram on the left shows you how to draw the object step by step. Simply follow along drawing in the space provided on the right-hand side. Add each detail as shown until the picture is finished.

Start off drawing lightly and don't worry about making mistakes. You can always erase and start over.

When you're finished, you can add your own details and color it!

Have fun!

Car

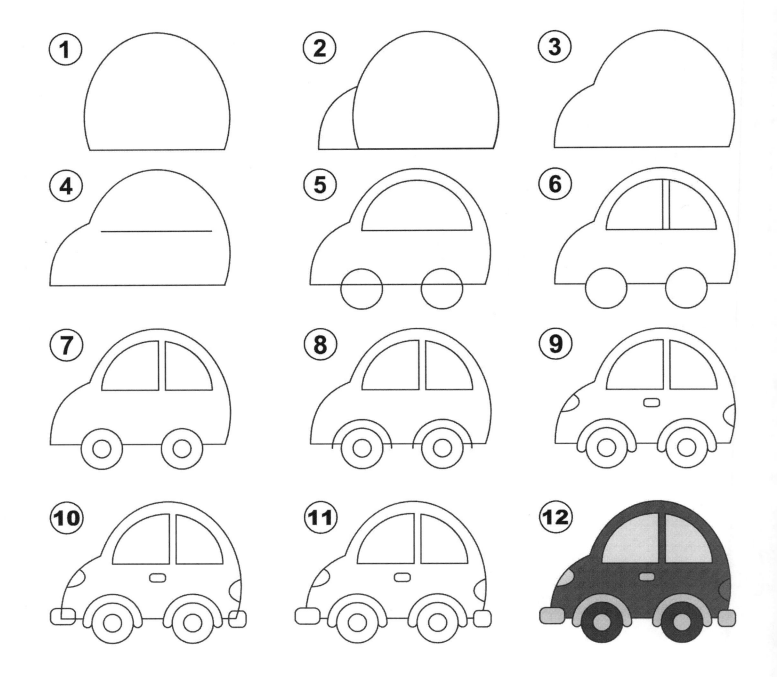

Your Turn to Draw

Dump Truck

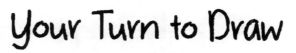

Your Turn to Draw

Sailboat

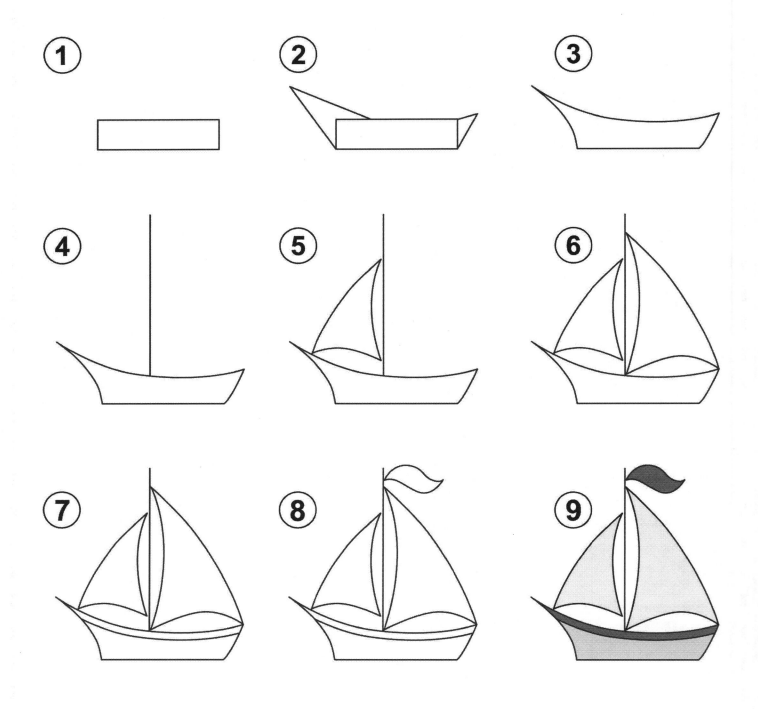

Your Turn to Draw

Rocket

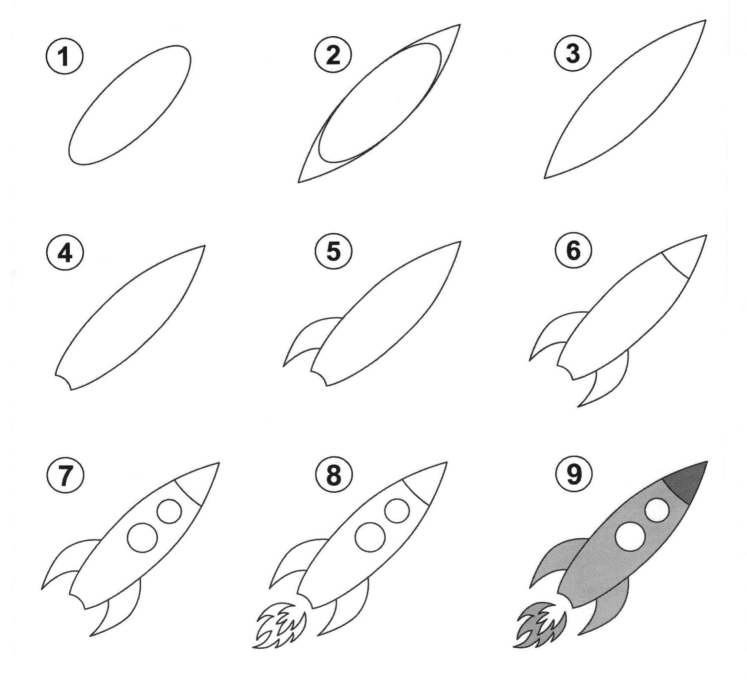

Your Turn to Draw

Train

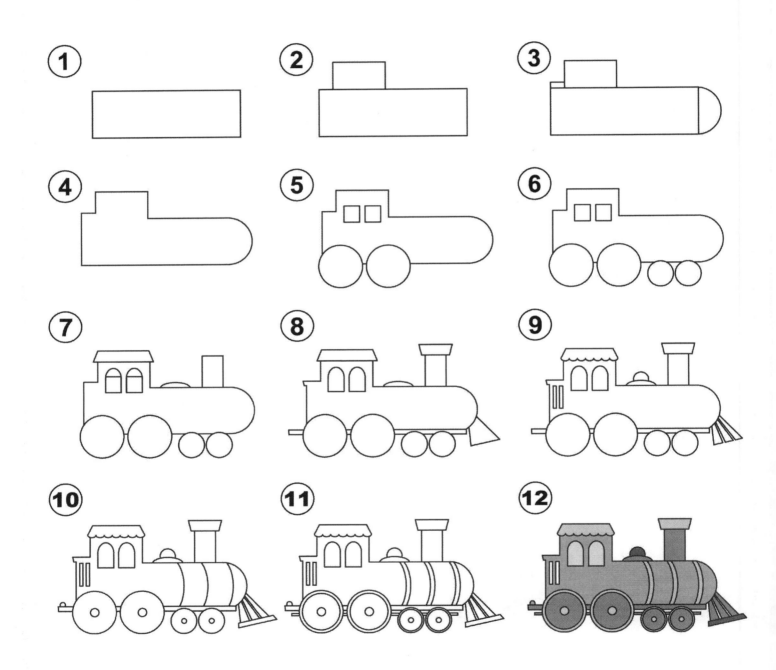

Your Turn to Draw

Submarine

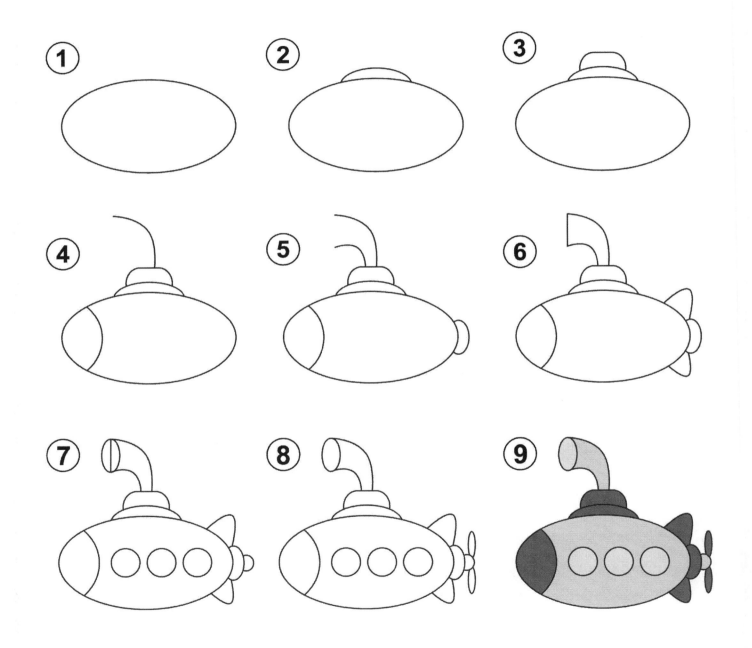

Your Turn to Draw

Spaceship

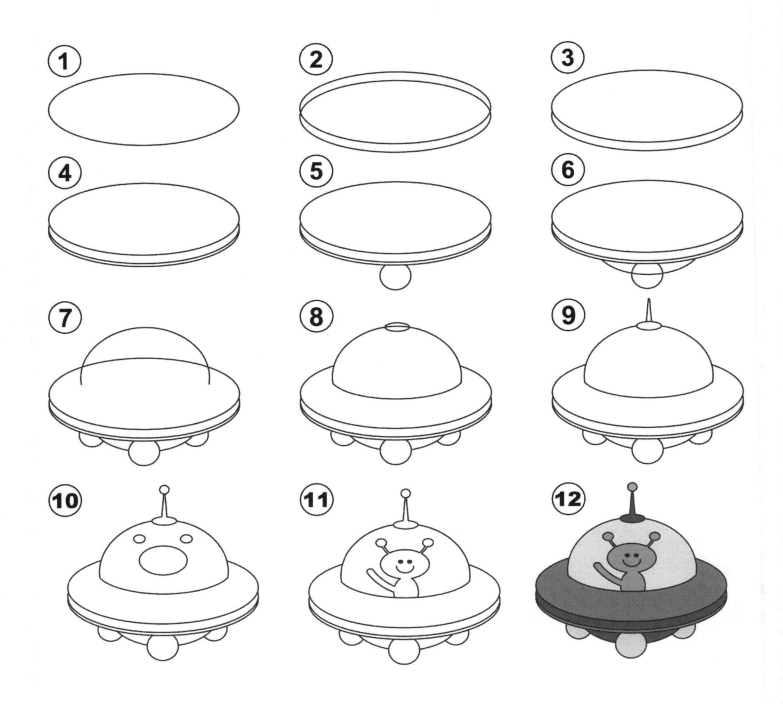

Your Turn to Draw

Train

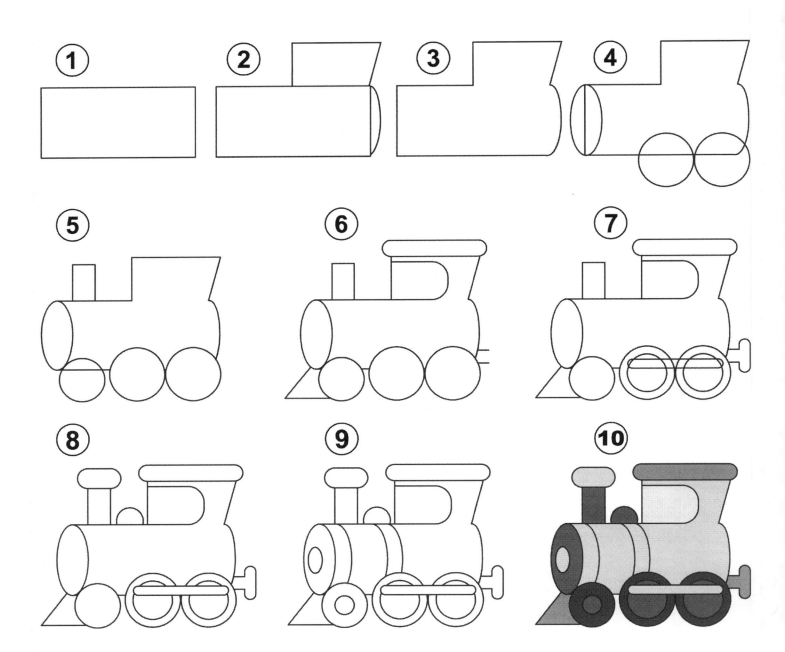

Your Turn to Draw

Blimp

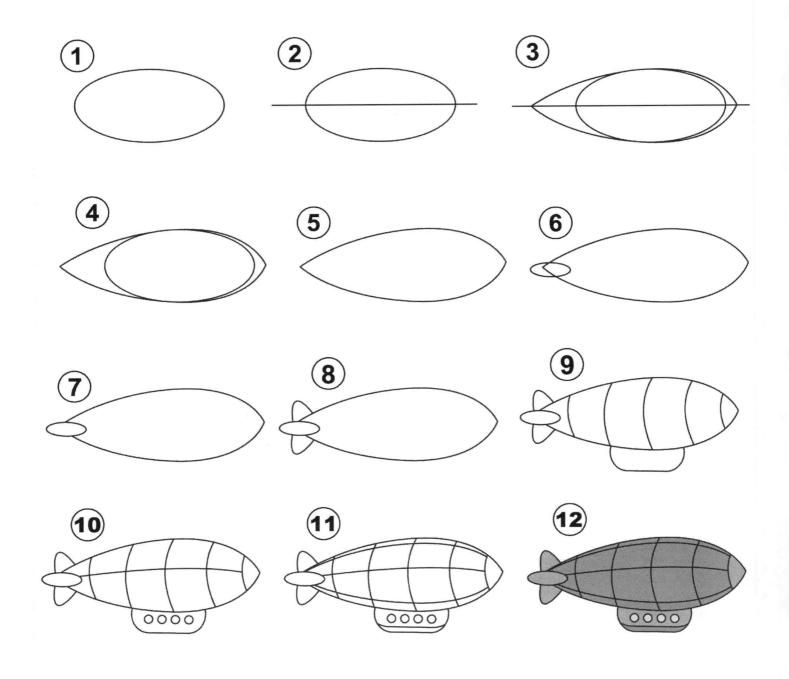

Your Turn to Draw

Motorcycle

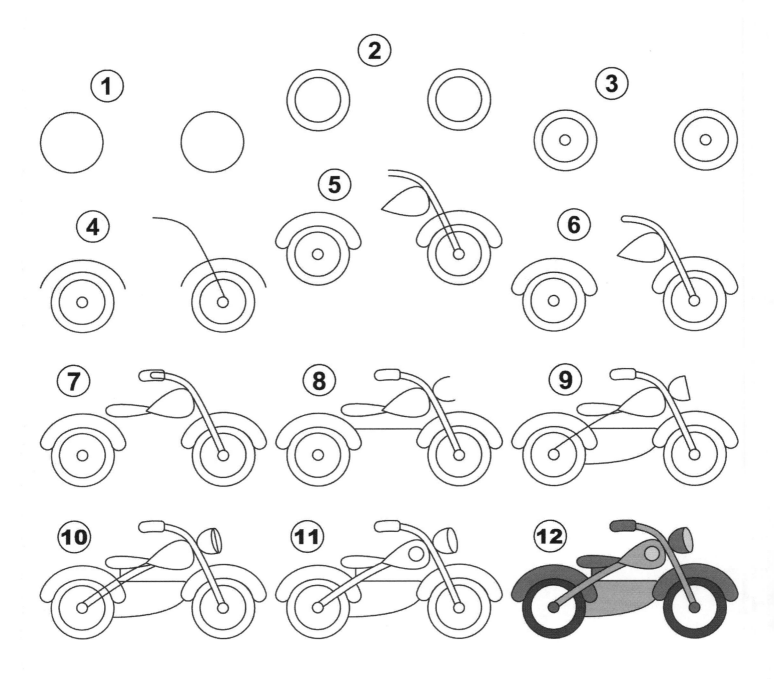

Your Turn to Draw

Helicopter

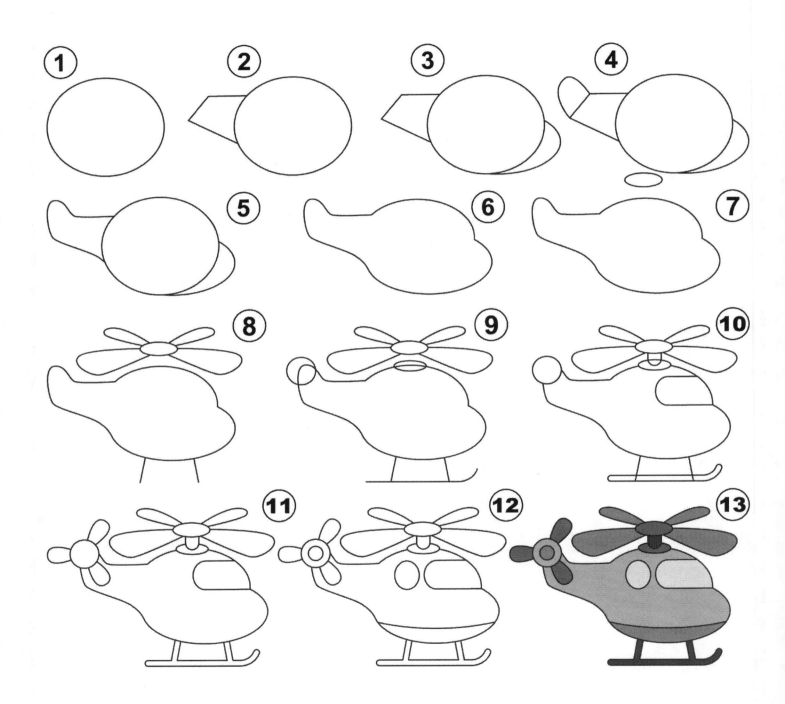

Your Turn to Draw

Hot Air Balloon

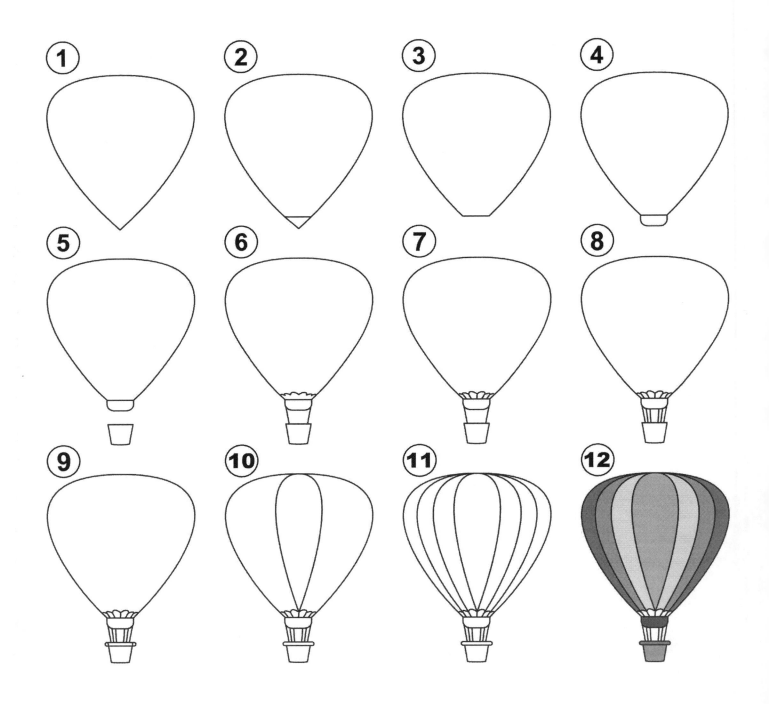

Your Turn to Draw

Bus

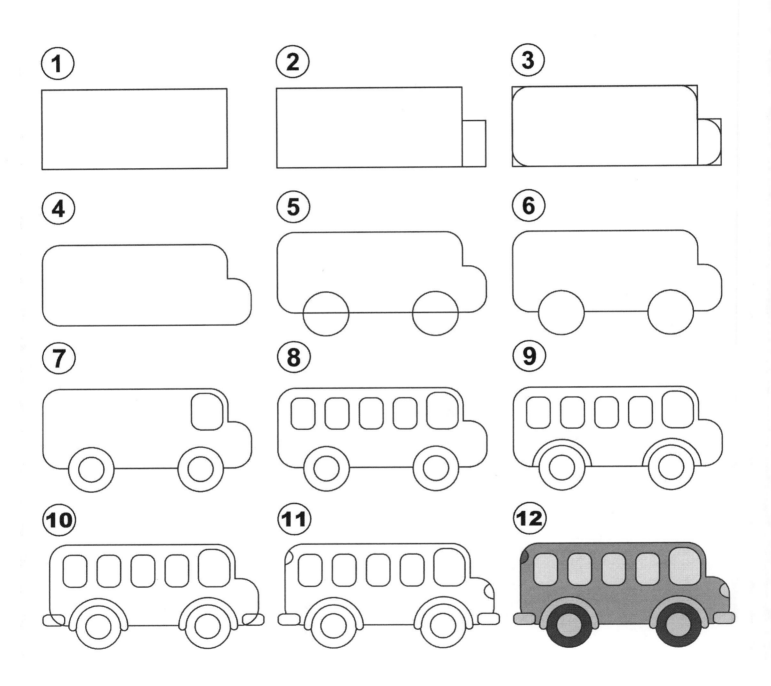

Your Turn to Draw

Truck

Your Turn to Draw

Digger

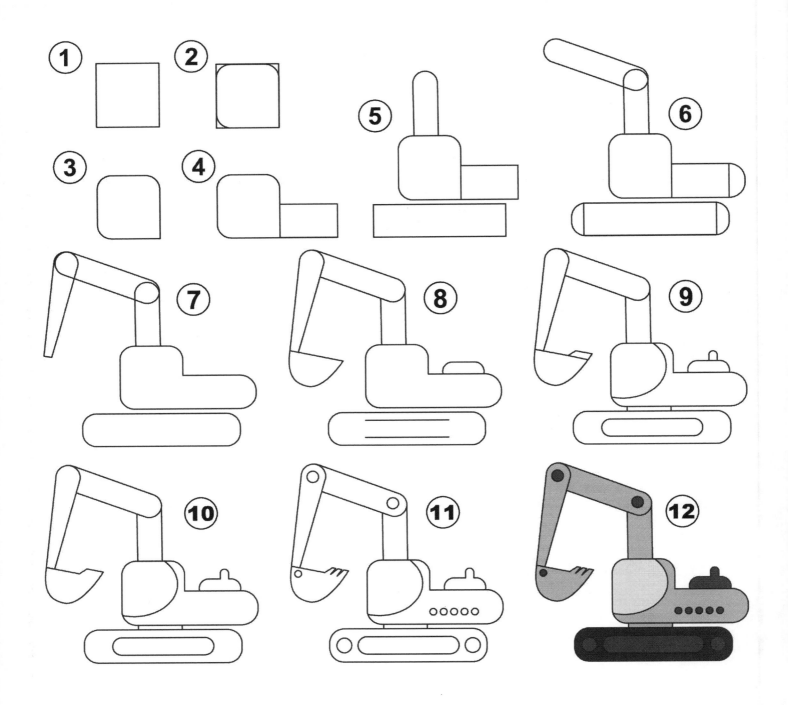

Your Turn to Draw

Plane

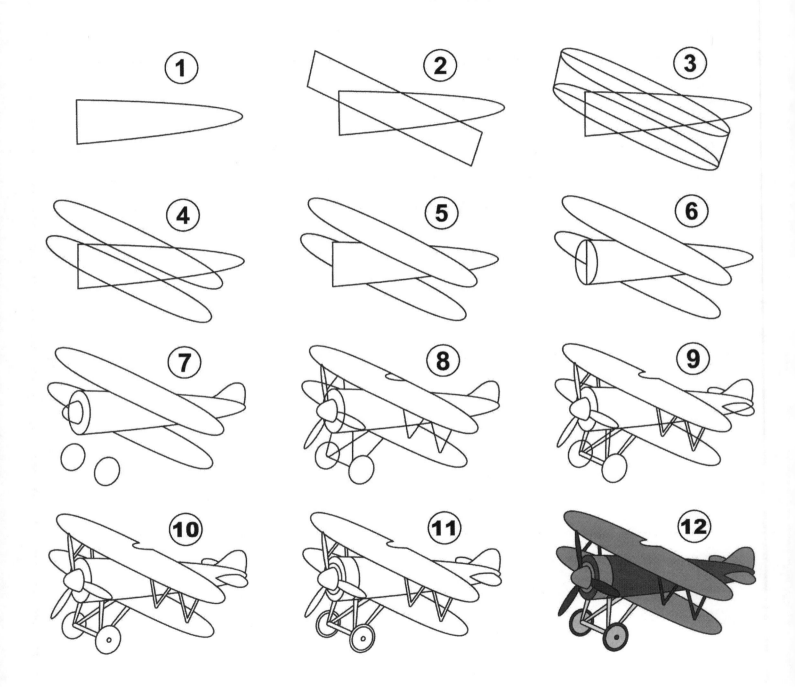

Your Turn to Draw

Four Wheeler

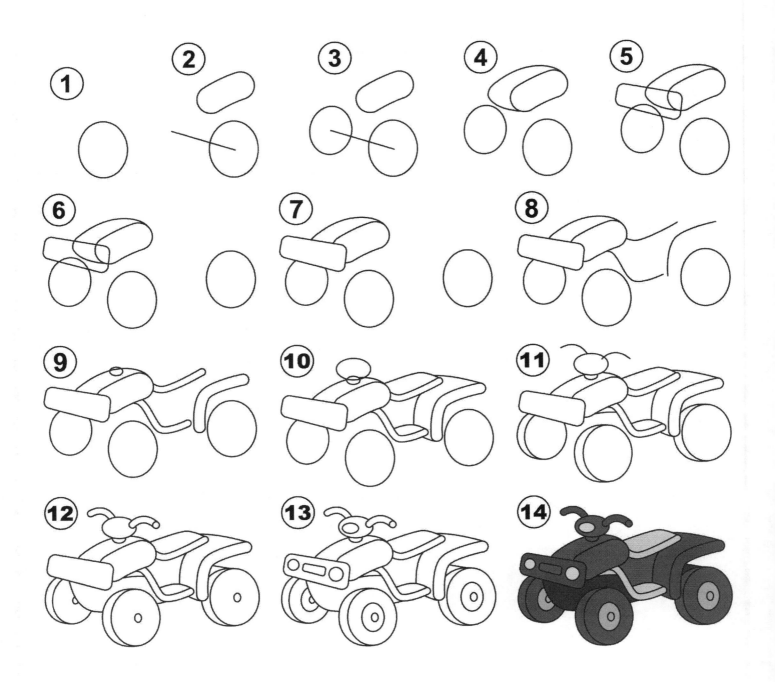

Your Turn to Draw

Dump Truck

Your Turn to Draw

Bicycle

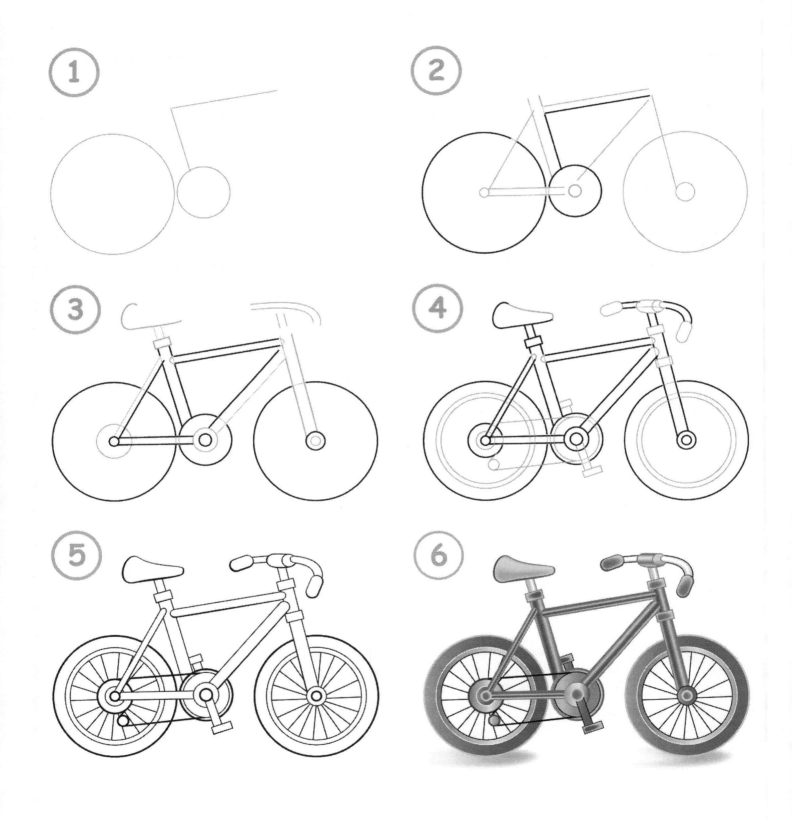

Your Turn to Draw

Tractor

Your Turn to Draw

Sailboat

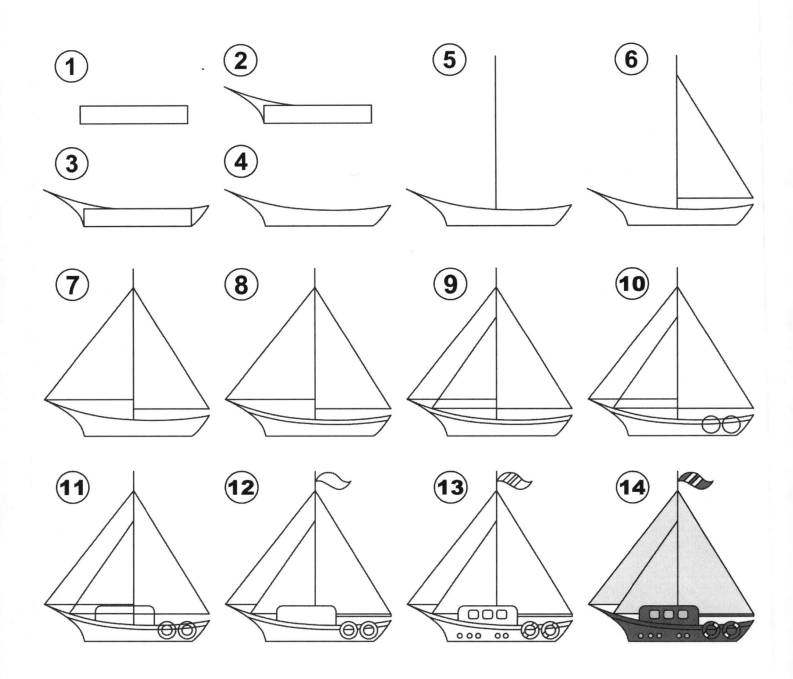

Your Turn to Draw

Rocket

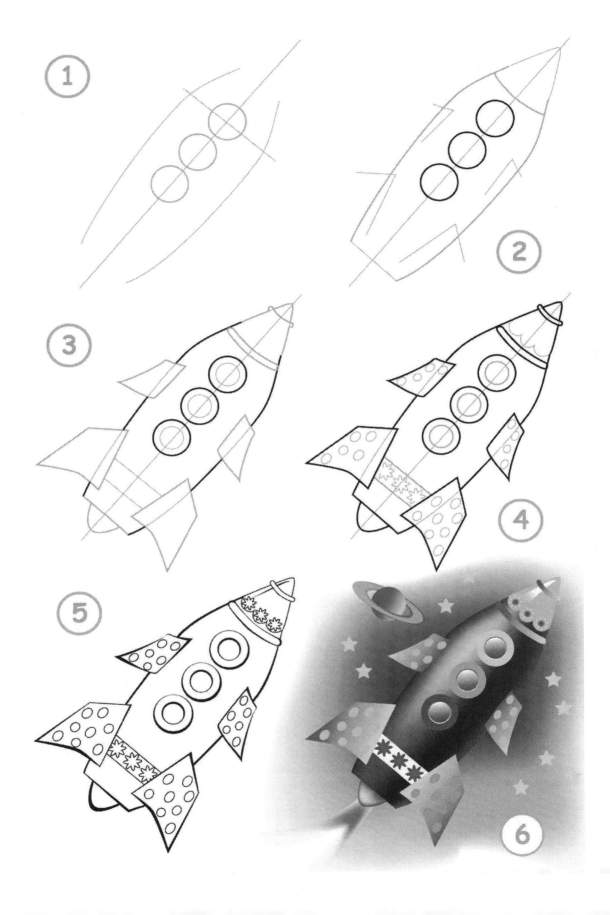

Your Turn to Draw

Tow Truck

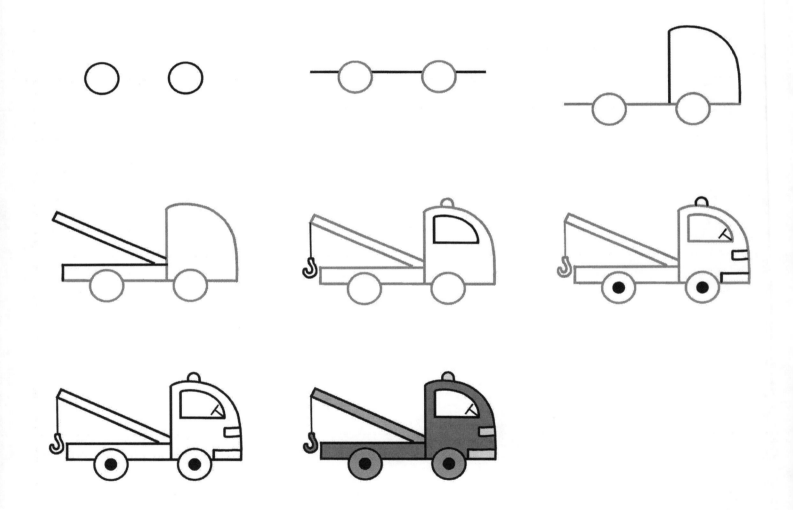

Motorcycle

Your Turn to Draw

Jet Plane

Your Turn to Draw

Car

Your Turn to Draw

Pickup Truck

1

2

3

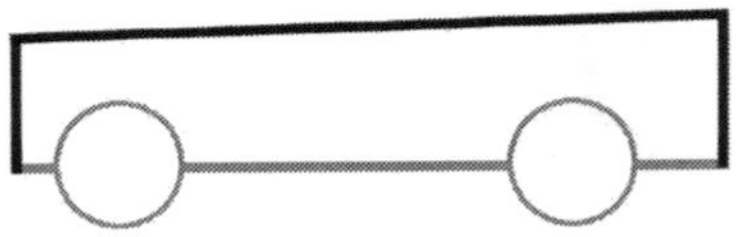

4

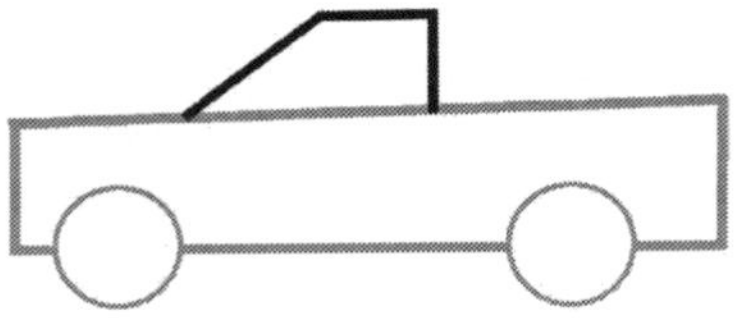

5

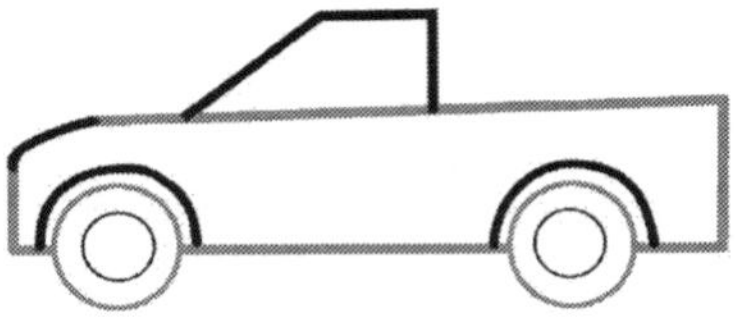

6

7

8

Your Turn to Draw

Road Roller Truck

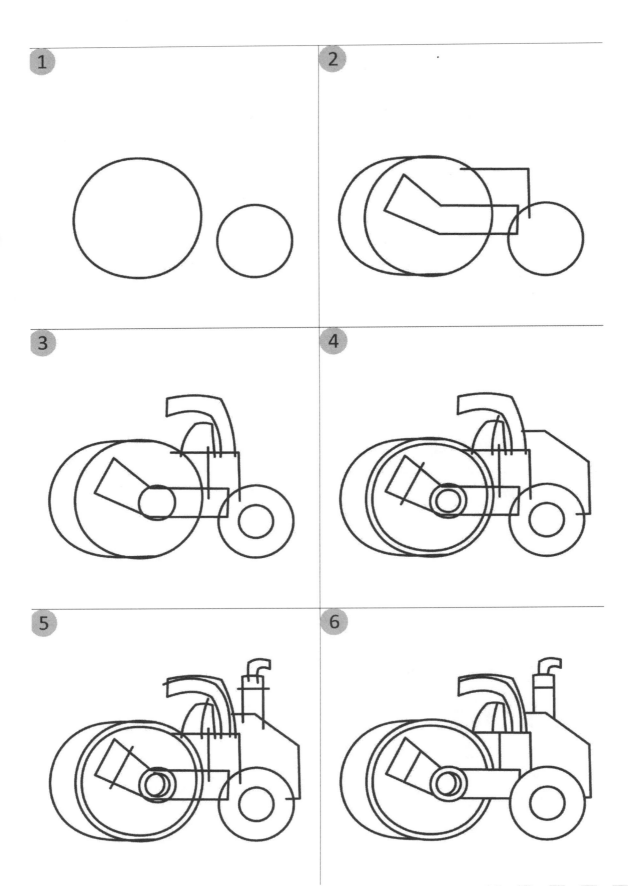

Your Turn to Draw

Made in the USA
Monee, IL
16 December 2024

74066034R00033